Ed Sheeran:

CW00351492

Published by
Wise Publications
14-15 Berners Street,
London W1T 3LJ, UK.

Exclusive Distributors:
Music Sales Limited
Distribution Centre,
Newmarket Road,
Bury St Edmunds,
Suffolk IP33 3YB, UK.

Music Sales Pty Limited
20 Resolution Drive,
Caringbah, NSW 2229,
Australia.

Order No. AM1004982
ISBN: 978-1-78038-645-4
This book © Copyright 2012
Wise Publications, a division
of Music Sales Limited.

Edited by Adrian Hopkins.
Music arranged by Arthur Dick.
Music processed by
Paul Ewers Music Design.

Printed in the EU.

WISE PUBLICATIONS
part of The Music Sales Group
London / New York / Paris / Sydney / Copenhagen / Berlin / Madrid / Hong Kong / Tokyo

Guitar Tablature Explained

Guitar music can be notated in three different ways: on a musical stave, in tablature, and in rhythm slashes

RHYTHM SLASHES: are written above the stave. Strum chords in the rhythm indicated. Round noteheads indicate single notes.

THE MUSICAL STAVE: shows pitches and rhythms and is divided by lines into bars. Pitches are named after the first seven letters of the alphabet.

TABLATURE: graphically represents the guitar fingerboard. Each horizontal line represents a string, and each number represents a fret.

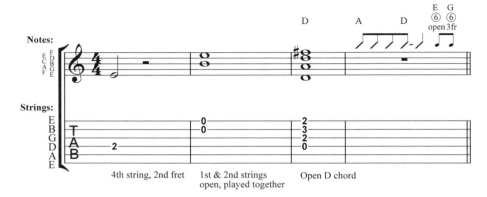

Notes:

Strings:

4th string, 2nd fret | 1st & 2nd strings open, played together | Open D chord

Definitions for special guitar notation

SEMI-TONE BEND: Strike the note and bend up a semi-tone (½ step).

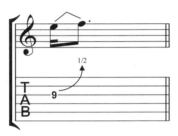

WHOLE-TONE BEND: Strike the note and bend up a whole-tone (full step).

GRACE NOTE BEND: Strike the note and bend as indicated. Play the first note as quickly as possible.

QUARTER-TONE BEND: Strike the note and bend up a ¼ step

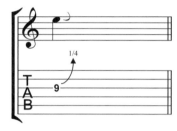

BEND & RELEASE: Strike the note and bend up as indicated, then release back to the original note.

COMPOUND BEND & RELEASE: Strike the note and bend up and down in the rhythm indicated.

PRE-BEND: Bend the note as indicated, then strike it.

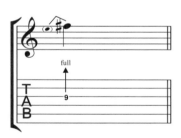

PRE-BEND & RELEASE: Bend the note as indicated. Strike it and release the note back to the original pitch.

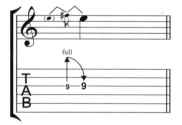

HAMMER-ON: Strike the first note with one finger, then sound the second note (on the same string) with another finger by fretting it without picking.

PULL-OFF: Place both fingers on the note to be sounded, strike the first note and without picking, pull the finger off to sound the second note.

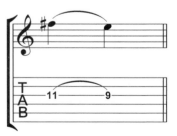

LEGATO SLIDE (GLISS): Strike the first note and then slide the same fret-hand finger up or down to the second note. The second note is not struck.

MUFFLED STRINGS: A percussive sound is produced by laying the first hand across the string(s) without depressing, and striking them with the pick hand.

NATURAL HARMONIC: Strike the note while the fret-hand lightly touches the string directly over the fret indicated.

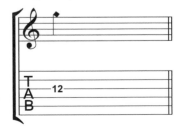

PICK SCRAPE: The edge of the pick is rubbed down (or up) the string, producing a scratchy sound.

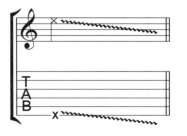

PALM MUTING: The note is partially muted by the pick hand lightly touching the string(s) just before the bridge.

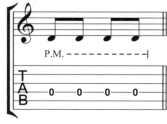

SHIFT SLIDE (GLISS & RESTRIKE) Same as legato slide, except the second note is struck.

2

TAP HARMONIC: The note is fretted normally and a harmonic is produced by tapping or slapping the fret indicated in brackets (which will be twelve frets higher than the fretted note.)

TAPPING: Hammer ('tap') the fret indicated with the pick-hand index or middle finger and pull-off to the note fretted by the fret hand.

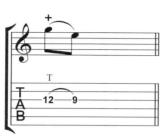

PINCH HARMONIC: The note is fretted normally and a harmonic is produced by adding the edge of the thumb or the tip of the index finger of the pick hand to the normal pick attack.

ARTIFICIAL HARMONIC: The note fretted normally and a harmonic is produced by gently resting the pick hand's index finger directly above the indicated fret (in brackets) while plucking the appropriate string.

TRILL: Very rapidly alternate between the notes indicated by continuously hammering-on and pulling-off.

RAKE: Drag the pick across the strings with a single motion.

TREMOLO PICKING: The note is picked as rapidly and continuously as possible.

ARPEGGIATE: Play the notes of the chord indicated by quickly rolling them from bottom to top.

SWEEP PICKING: Rhythmic downstroke and/or upstroke motion across the strings.

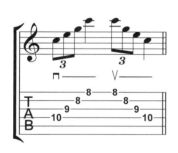

VIBRATO DIVE BAR AND RETURN: The pitch of the note or chord is dropped a specific number of steps (in rhythm) then returned to the original pitch.

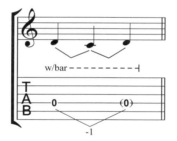

VIBRATO BAR SCOOP: Depress the bar just before striking the note, then quickly release the bar.

VIBRATO BAR DIP: Strike the note and then immediately drop a specific number of steps, then release back to the original pitch.

Additional musical definitions

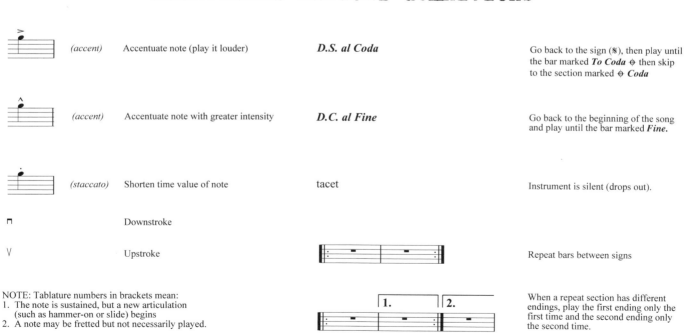

(accent) — Accentuate note (play it louder)

(accent) — Accentuate note with greater intensity

(staccato) — Shorten time value of note

⊓ — Downstroke

V — Upstroke

D.S. al Coda — Go back to the sign (𝄋), then play until the bar marked ***To Coda*** ✛ then skip to the section marked ✛ ***Coda***

D.C. al Fine — Go back to the beginning of the song and play until the bar marked ***Fine.***

tacet — Instrument is silent (drops out).

Repeat bars between signs

When a repeat section has different endings, play the first ending only the first time and the second ending only the second time.

NOTE: Tablature numbers in brackets mean:
1. The note is sustained, but a new articulation (such as hammer-on or slide) begins
2. A note may be fretted but not necessarily played.

The A Team

Words & Music by Ed Sheeran

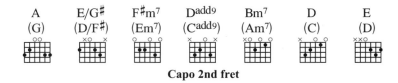

Capo 2nd fret

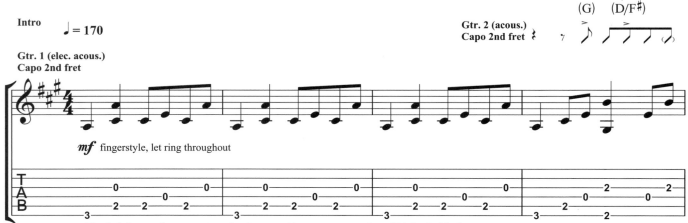

*Symbols in parentheses represent chord names with respect to capoed gtr. (Tab 0 = 2nd fret)
Symbols above represent actual sounding chords

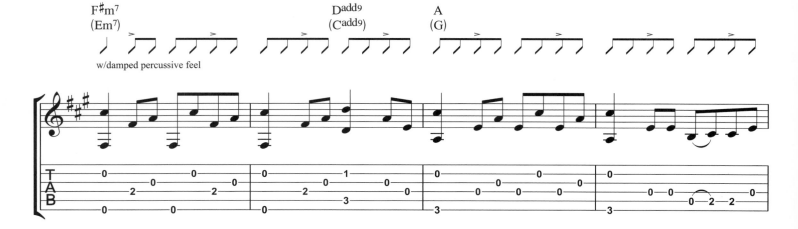

Verse

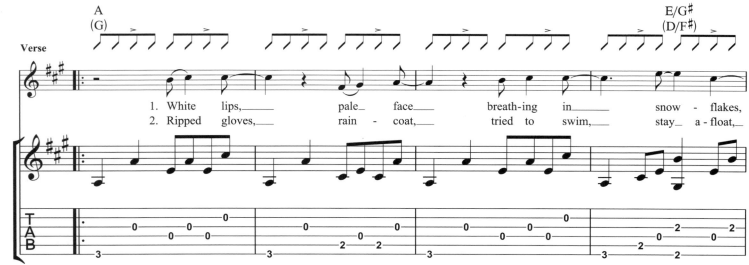

1. White lips,____ pale_ face____ breath-ing in____ snow - flakes,

2. Ripped gloves,____ rain - coat,____ tried to swim,____ stay a - float,

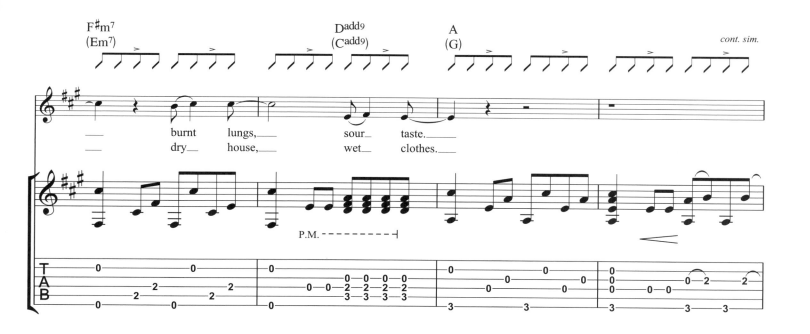

burnt lungs,___ sour taste.___
dry___ house,___ wet___ clothes.___

P.M. - - - - - - - - - -

Light's gone,___ day's___ end,___ strug-gl - ing___ to pay___ rent,
Loose change,___ bank___ notes,___ wear-y - eyed,___ dry___ throat,

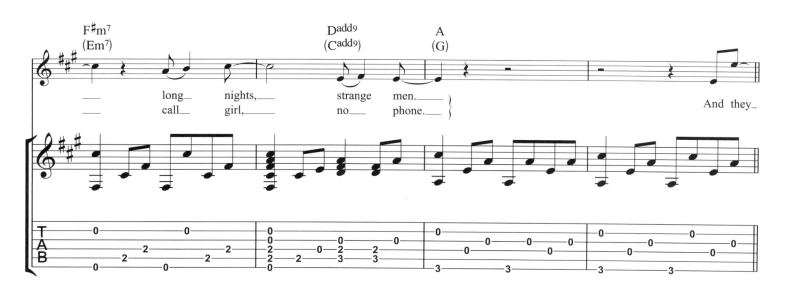

___ long___ nights,___ strange men.___
___ call___ girl,___ no___ phone.___

And they_

5

closed eyed___ and hop - ing for a bet - ter life. This___

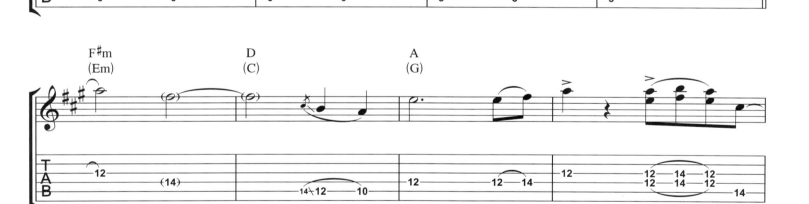

___ time, will fade out to - night, straight down the line.

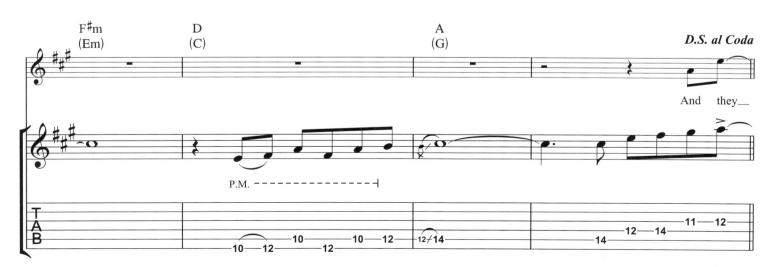

And they___

10

U.N.I

Words & Music by Ed Sheeran & Jake Gosling

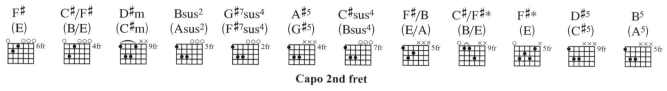

Capo 2nd fret

```
Gtr. 1
6 = E  3 = E
5 = A  2 = B
4 = D  1 = E
```

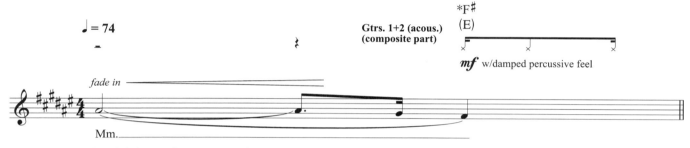

*Symbols in parentheses represent chord names with respect to capoed gtr. (Tab 0 = 2nd fret)
Symbols above represent actual sounding chords

Verse

1. I found your hair-band on my bed-room floor,

the on-ly ev-i-dence that you've been here be-fore
but I know that, I nev-er wan-na set-tle down, come a-round, break up the love like Le-go now,

Nev-er wan-na turn in-to a-noth-er like you, sleep with my thoughts, dance with my views.
and I don't get waves of miss-ing you an-y-more.

they're more like___ tsu - na - mi tides in my eyes, nev - er
Ev - 'ry-thing's great, not ev - 'ry-thing's sure, but you live in your halls and I live in a tour bus.

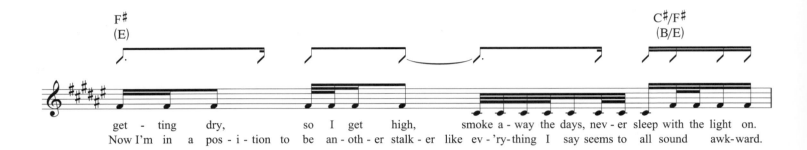

get - ting dry, so I get high, smoke a - way the days, nev - er sleep with the light on.
Now I'm in a pos - i - tion to be an - oth - er stalk - er like ev - 'ry-thing I say seems to all sound awk-ward.

Weeks pass in the blink of an eye and I'm still drunk at the end of the night.
like our last kiss it was per - fect we were ner - vous on the sur - face.

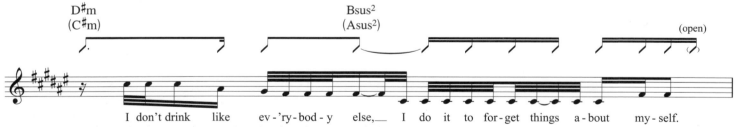

I don't drink like ev - 'ry-bod - y else,___ I do it to for - get things a - bout my - self.
And I'm al - ways say-ing ev - 'ry-day that it was worth it, pain is on - ly rel - e - vant if it still hurts. I for-

Stum-ble and fall with the head spin I got,___ my mind's with you but my heart's just not.
-get like an el - e-phant or we can use a sed - a-tive and go back to the day we fell in love just on our first kiss.

12

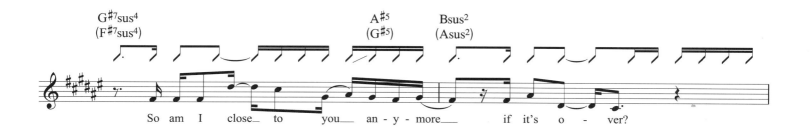

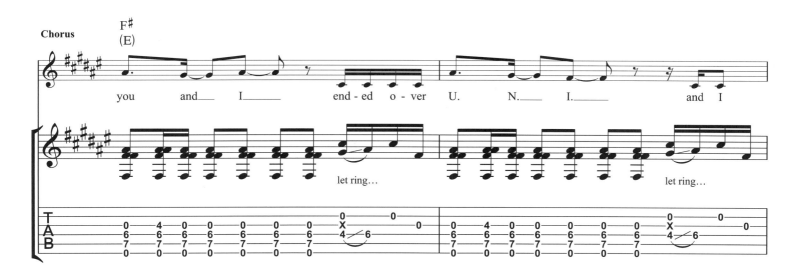

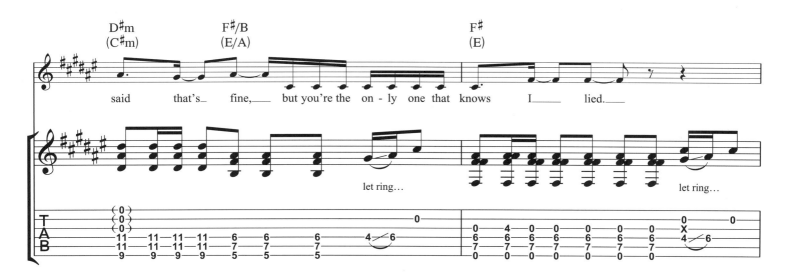

15

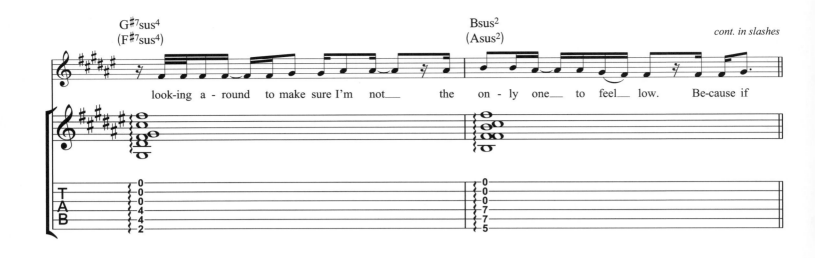

cont. in slashes

look-ing a - round to make sure I'm not___ the on - ly one___ to feel___ low. Be-cause if

you_____ want___ I'll take you in___ my arms___ and keep___ you

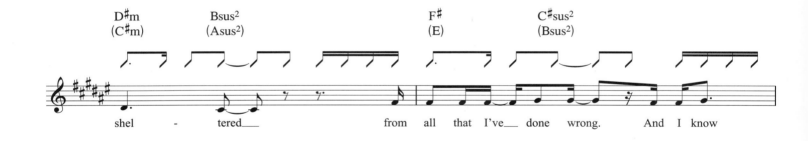

shel - tered___ from all that I've___ done wrong. And I know

you'll___ say___ that I'm the on - ly one.___ But I___ know

cont. in stave

God made a - noth-er one of me to love you bet - ter than I___ ev - er will. 'Cause

16

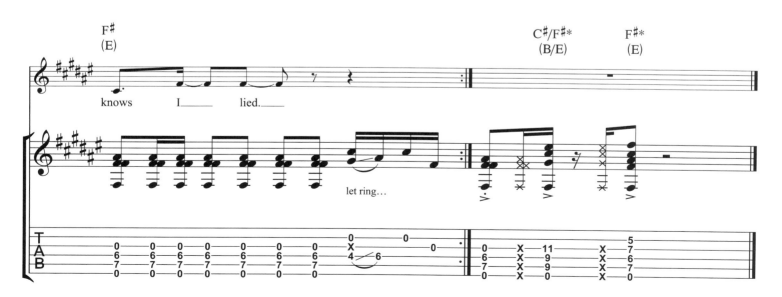

Drunk

Words & Music by Ed Sheeran & Jake Gosling

did-n't kill me,_____ it nev-er made me strong - er at all._____
I know I'll nev-er hold____ you like I used_ to.
Though I know_____ you'll nev-er love___ me___ like you used_ to.
- fore, and you don't hold me a-ny-more.

But a
On__

Pre-chorus

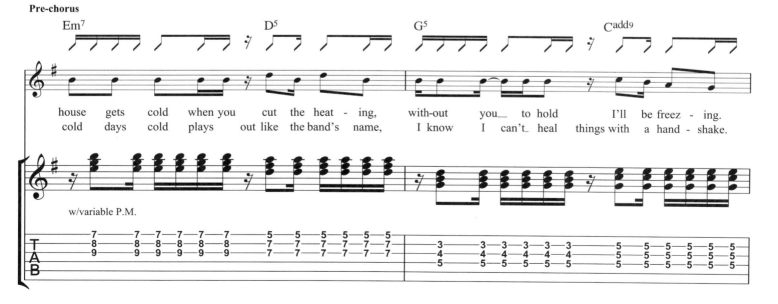

house gets cold when you cut the heat - ing, with-out you__ to hold I'll be freez - ing.
cold days cold plays out like the band's name, I know I can't_ heal things with a hand - shake.

w/variable P.M.

19

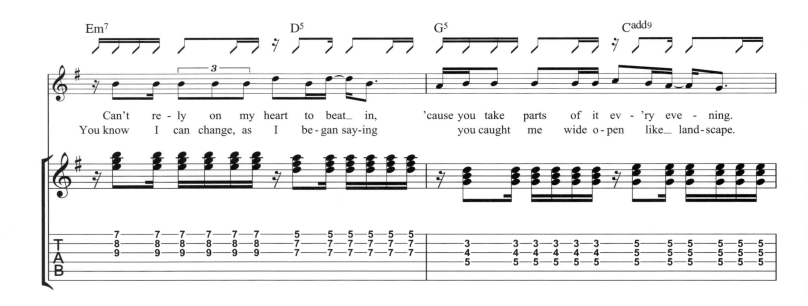

Can't re-ly on my heart to beat_ in, 'cause you take parts of it ev-'ry eve - ning.
You know I can change, as I be-gan say-ing you caught me wide o-pen like_ land-scape.

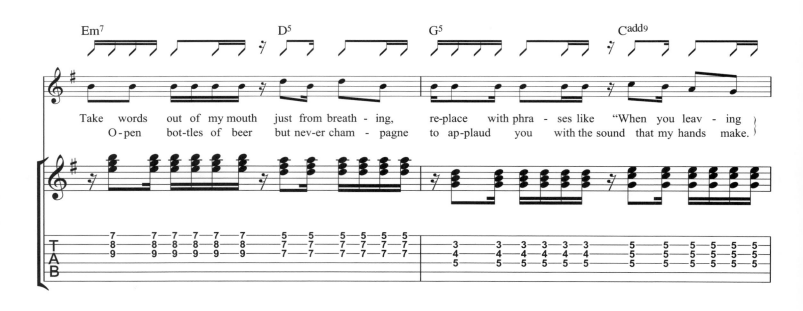

Take words out of my mouth just from breath - ing, re-place with phra - ses like "When you leav - ing
O-pen bot-tles of beer but nev-er cham - pagne to ap-plaud you with the sound that my hands make."

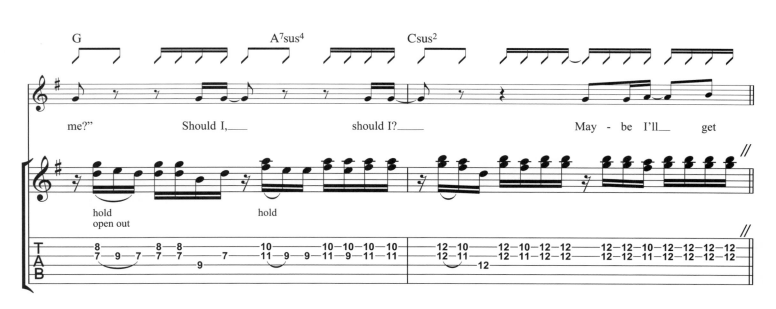

me?" Should I,___ should I?___ May - be I'll get

hold
hold
open out

Chorus

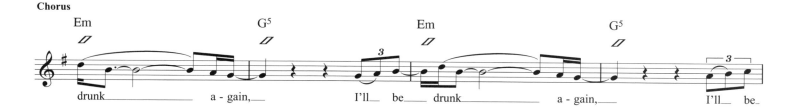

drunk_____ a - gain,____ I'll be____ drunk_____ a - gain,____ I'll be_

____ drunk_____ a - gain____ to feel a lit - tle love._____

All__ by____ my - self,____ I'm here___ a-gain. All__ by____ my - self,_

____ you know I'll nev-er change.__ All by____ my - self,____

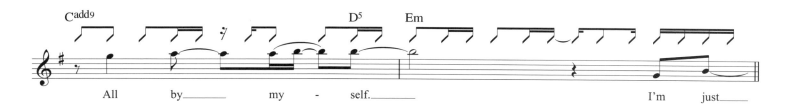

All by_____ my - self._____ I'm just____

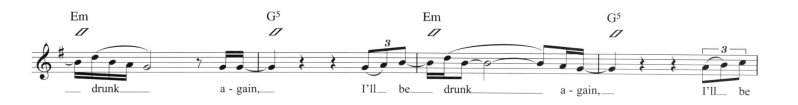

____ drunk_____ a - gain,____ I'll be____ drunk_____ a - gain,____ I'll be

drunk_____ a - gain____ to feel a lit - tle love._____

21

Grade 8

Words & Music by Ed Sheeran, Robert Conlon & Sukhdeep Uppal

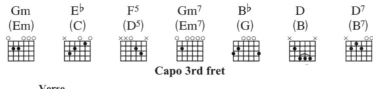

Capo 3rd fret

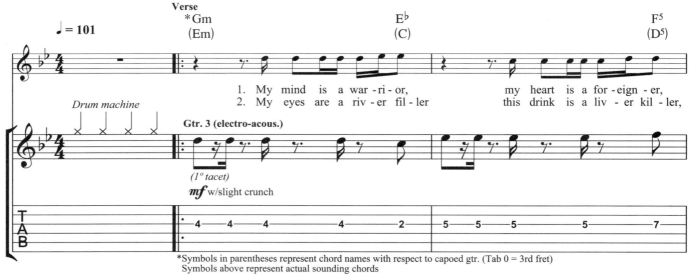

*Symbols in parentheses represent chord names with respect to capoed gtr. (Tab 0 = 3rd fret)
Symbols above represent actual sounding chords

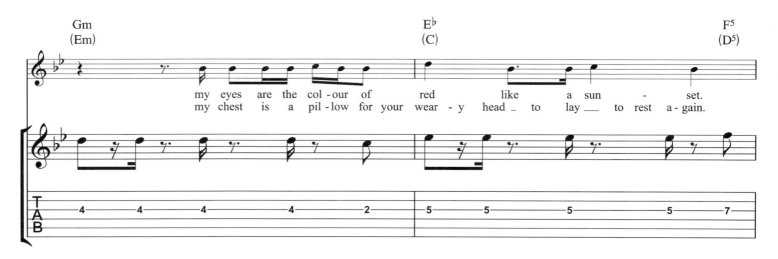

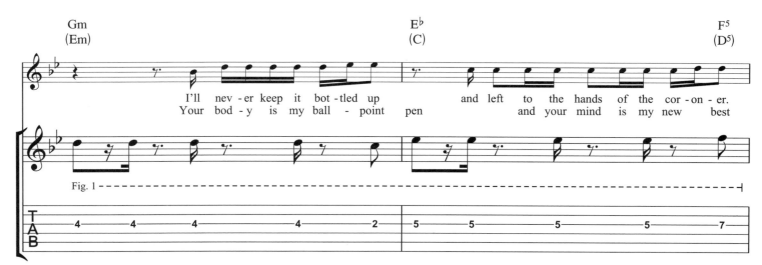

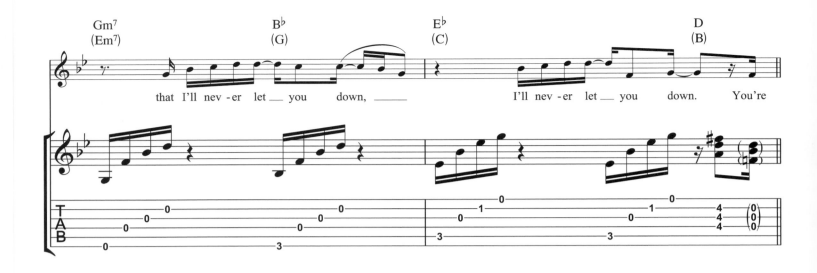

that I'll nev -er let ___ you down, ___ I'll nev -er let ___ you down. You're

Chorus

Gtr. 2 (acous.)

cont. strumming 16ths, percussive feel

strum -ming on my heart strings like you were a grade 8 but I've nev -er felt this way. I'll pick your feet ___

Gtr. 3 plays Fig. 1 loop

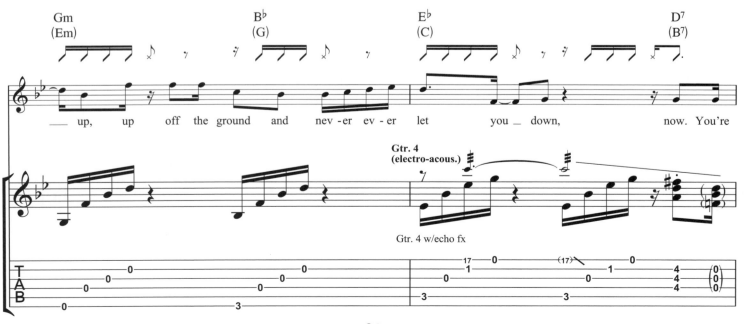

___ up, up off the ground and nev -er ev -er let you ___ down, now. You're

Gtr. 4 (electro-acous.)

Gtr. 4 w/echo fx

strum -ming on my heart strings like you were a grade 8 but I've nev -er felt this way. I'll pick your feet _

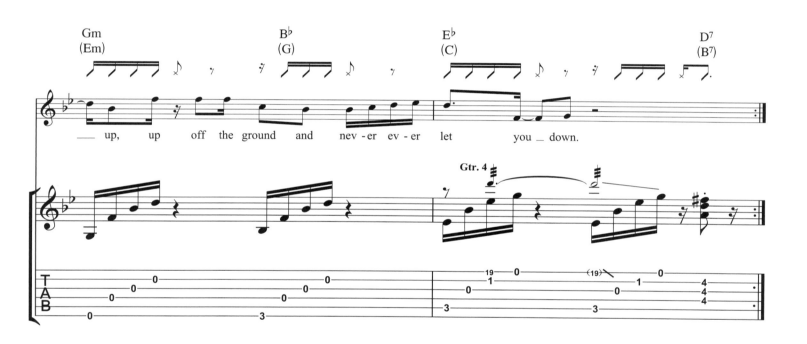

_ up, up off the ground and nev -er ev -er let you _ down.

Bridge

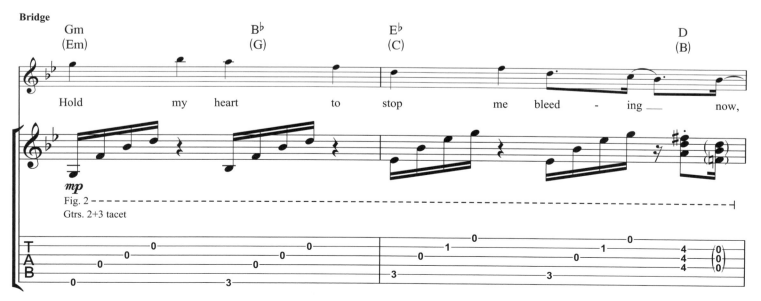

Hold my heart to stop me bleed - ing _ now,

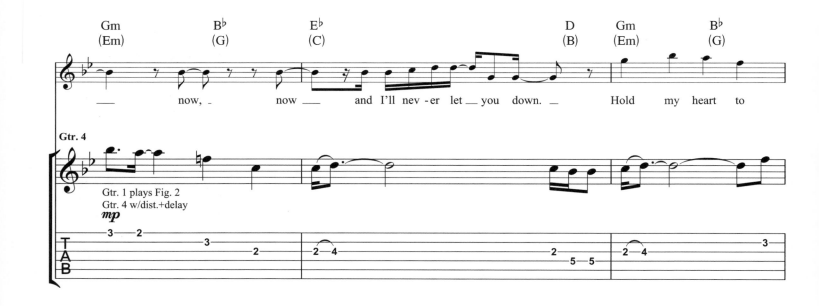

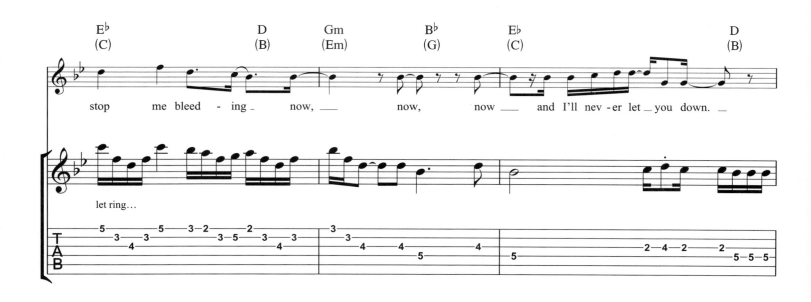

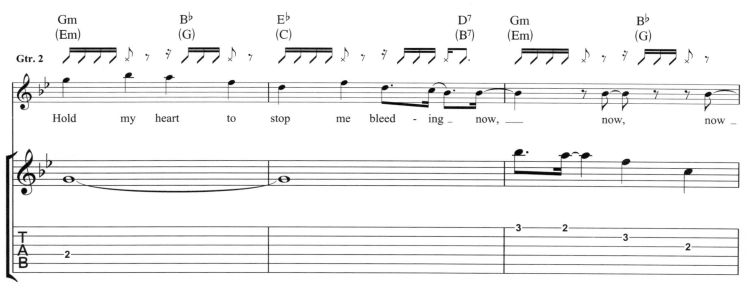

and I'll nev-er let _ you down. _ Hold my heart to stop me bleed-ing _ now,

_ now, _ now _ and I'll nev-er let _ you down. _ You're

Outro Chorus

Gtr. 2

cont. strumming 16ths, percussive feel

strum-ming on my heart strings like you were a grade 8 but I've nev-er felt this way. I'll pick your feet _

Gtr. 1

Gtr. 3 plays Fig. 1
Gtr. 4 tacet

Wake Me Up

Words & Music by Ed Sheeran & Jake Gosling

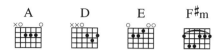

(Freely) ♩ = 96

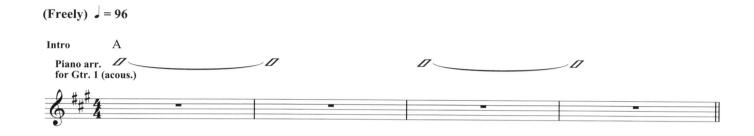

may - be you're love - a - ble_____ and may - be you're my snow - flake. And your eyes_

____ turn from green to grey_____ in the win - ter I'll hold you in a cold place. And

you should nev-er cut your hair 'cause I love the way_ you flick it off_your shoul - der. Mm._

Chorus

____ And you will nev-er know just how beau - ti - ful_ you are_ to me.

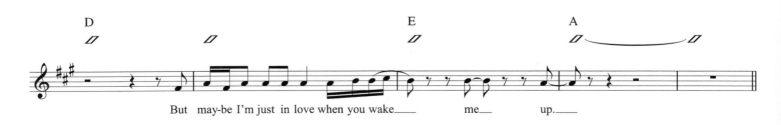

But may-be I'm just in love when you wake_____ me_ up._

30

Verse

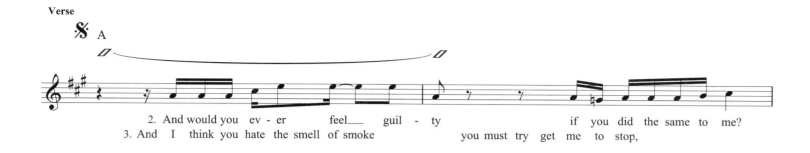

2. And would you ev - er feel___ guil - ty if you did the same to me?
3. And I think you hate the smell of smoke you must try get me to stop,

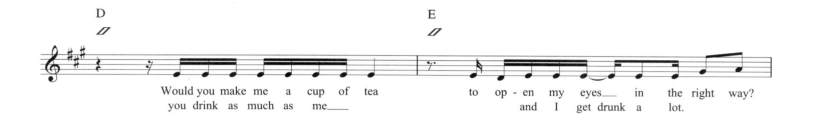

Would you make me a cup of tea to op - en my eyes___ in the right way?
you drink as much as me___ and I get drunk a lot.

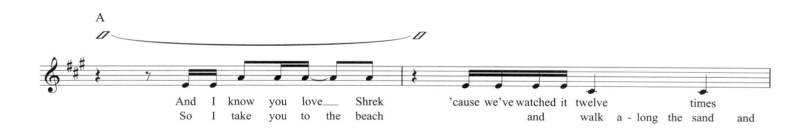

And I know you love___ Shrek 'cause we've watched it twelve times
So I take you to the beach and walk a - long the sand and

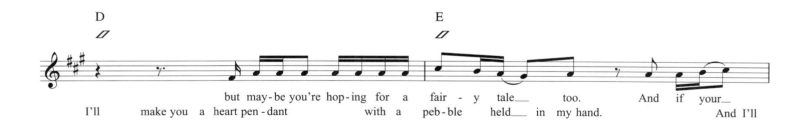

but may - be you're hop - ing for a fair - y tale___ too. And if your___
I'll make you a heart pen - dant with a peb - ble held___ in my hand. And I'll

D V D___ breaks to - day, you should have got a V C R,___
carve it like a neck - lace so the heart falls where your chest is

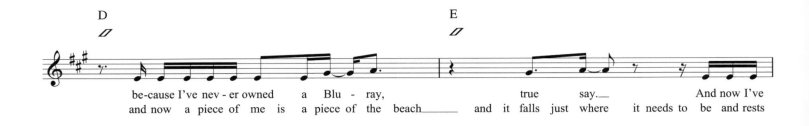

be-cause I've nev - er owned a Blu - ray, true say.— And now I've
and now a piece of me is a piece of the beach____ and it falls just where it needs to be and rests

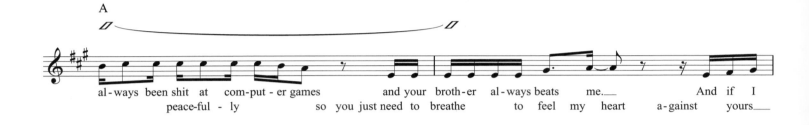

al - ways been shit at com - put - er games and your broth - er al - ways beats me.— And if I
peace - ful - ly so you just need to breathe to feel my heart a - gainst yours____

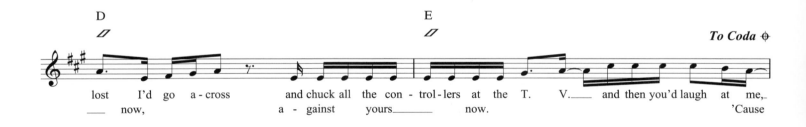

To Coda

lost I'd go a - cross and chuck all the con - trol - lers at the T. V.___ and then you'd laugh at me,
____ now, a - gainst yours____ now. 'Cause

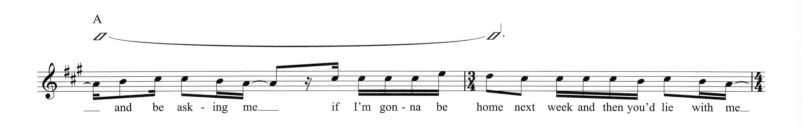

____ and be ask - ing me____ if I'm gon - na be home next week and then you'd lie with me____

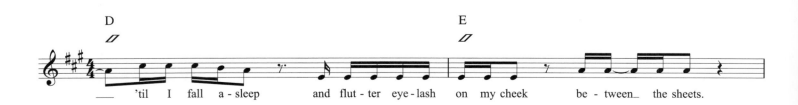

____ 'til I fall a - sleep and flut - ter eye - lash on my cheek be - tween_ the sheets.

Chorus

And you will nev-er know just how beau-ti-ful you are to me.

But

may-be I'm just in love when you wake me up.

D.S. al Coda

$\oplus$ *Coda*

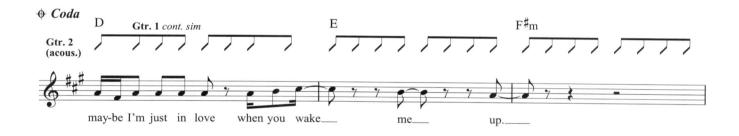

may-be I'm just in love when you wake me up.

Or may-be I'm just in love when you wake me up, woah.

rit.

Mm, may-be I fell in love when you woke me up.

Small Bump

Words & Music by Ed Sheeran

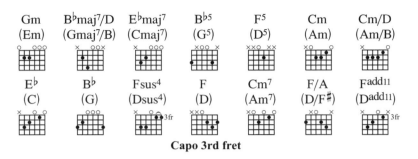

Capo 3rd fret

Intro ♩ = 120

Drums

cont. sim

Gtr. 1+2 (acous.)
composite part

†Gm
(Em)

mf

w/percussive feel

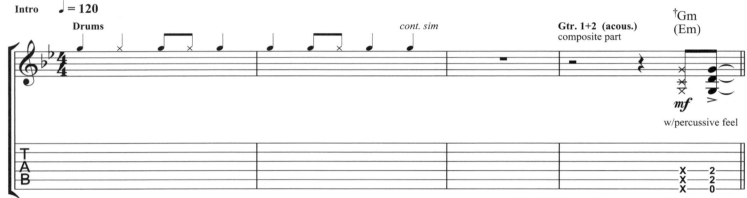

†Symbols in parentheses represent chord names
with respect to capoed gtr. (Tab 0 = 3rd fret)
Symbols above represent actual sounding chords

let ring…

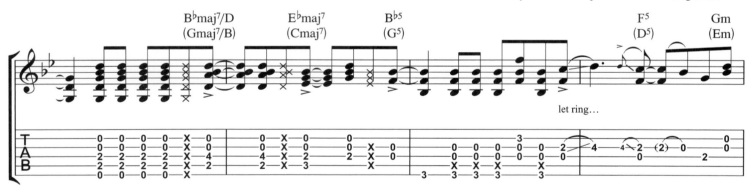

1. You're just a small

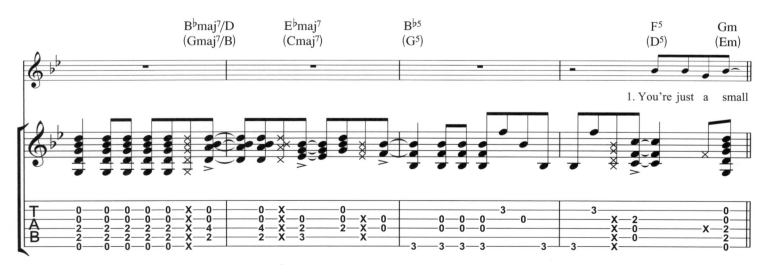

38

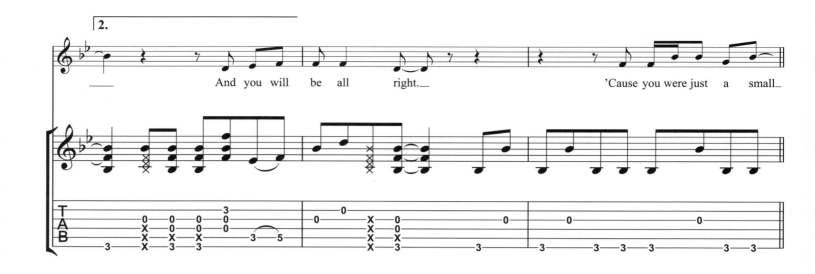

2.

And you will be all right.___ 'Cause you were just a small___

Outro

Gm
(Em)   B♭maj⁷/D   E♭maj⁷   B♭
                        (Gmaj⁷/B)   (Cmaj⁷)   (G)

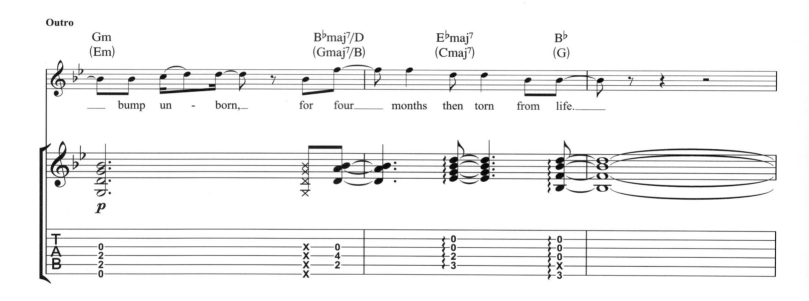

___ bump un - born,   for four___ months then torn   from life.___

p

Gm   *rit.*
(Em)   B♭maj⁷/D   E♭maj⁷   B♭
                        (Gmaj⁷/B)   (Cmaj⁷)   (G)

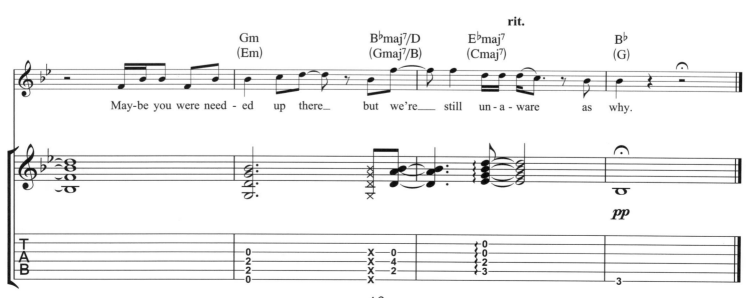

May-be you were need - ed   up there___   but we're___ still   un - a - ware   as   why.

pp

The City

Words & Music by Ed Sheeran & Jake Gosling

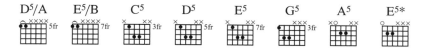

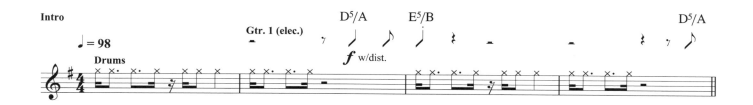

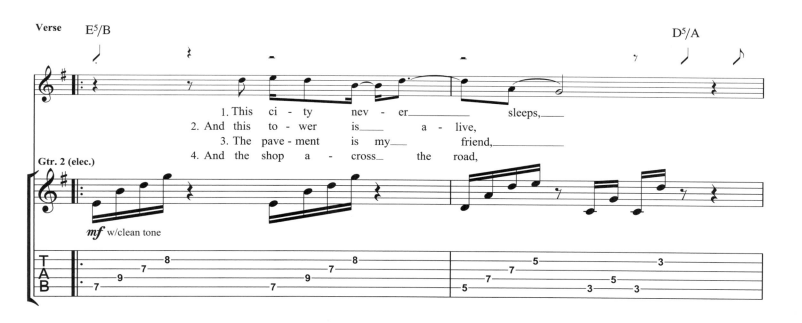

Si - rens bleed through my win - dow - sill,_____ I can't close my eyes._
Hood up and lace un - tied, and sleep fills my mind.
I find it trips me up_____ and puts me down.
Voi - ces speak through my walls,_____ I don't think I'm gon - na make it

1, 3.

Don't con - trol_ what I'm in - to._____
Can't con - trol_ what I'm
This is not_ what I'm used to.
past to - mor - row._

2, 4.

in - to._

tacet on 𝄋
tacet on 𝄋

Lon - don calls_____ me a stran - ger,_____ a tra - vel - ler.

pp

On 𝄋 play single chord spreads for six bars

42

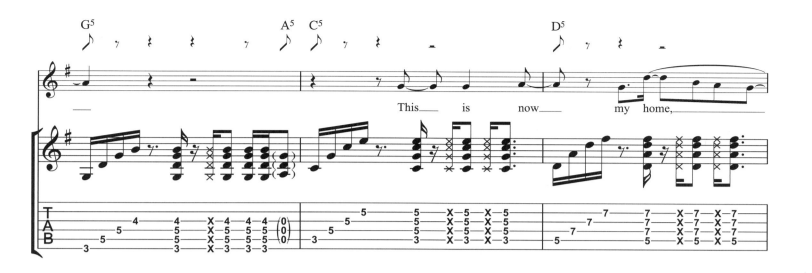

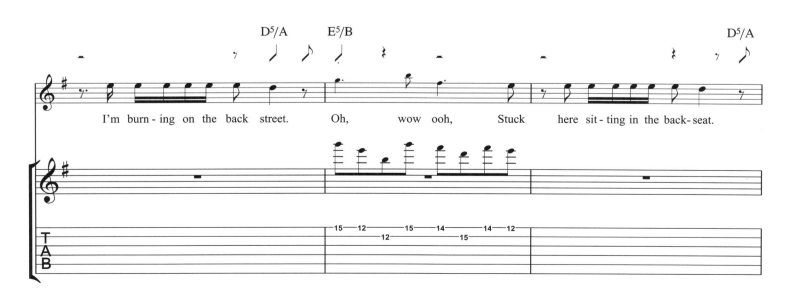

Oh, wow ooh, I'm blaz - ing on the street.___ What I do___ is - n't up to you___ if the

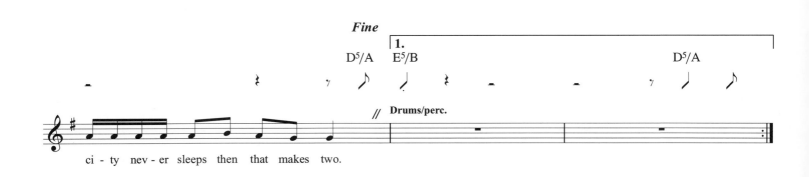

ci - ty nev - er sleeps then that makes two.

And my lungs hurt, and my ears___ bled,

This

Words & Music by Ed Sheeran & Gordon Mills

*Symbols in parentheses represent chord names with respect to capoed gtr. (Tab 0 = 4th fret)
Symbols above represent actual sounding chords

1. This   is   the start   of some-thing_ beau-ti-ful._

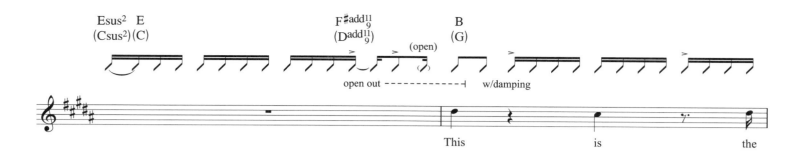

This is the

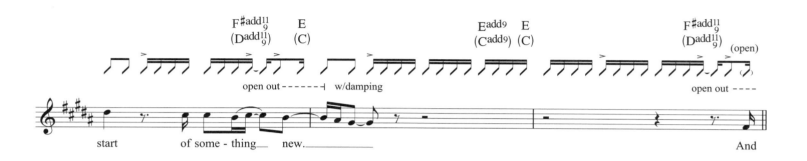

start of some - thing___ new.

And

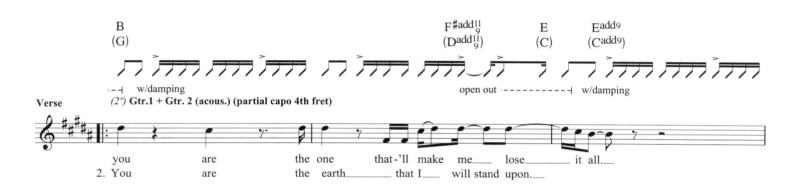

you are the one that-'ll make me___ lose_____ it all.

2. You are the earth_____ that I___ will stand upon.___

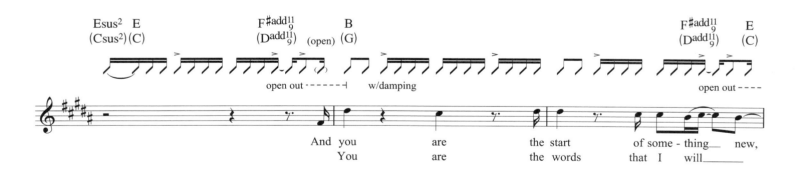

And you are the start of some - thing___ new,

You are the words that I will_____

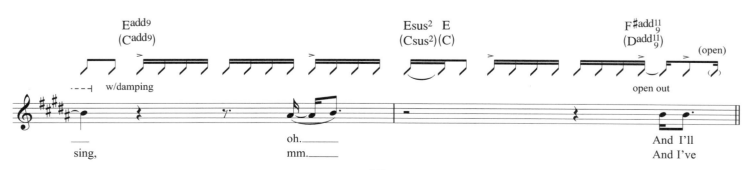

___ sing,

2. oh.___

mm.___

And I'll

And I've

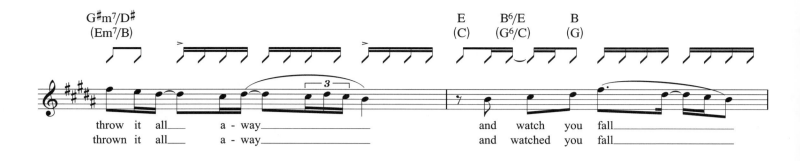

throw it all___ a - way_____ and watch you fall_____
thrown it all___ a - way_____ and watched you fall_____

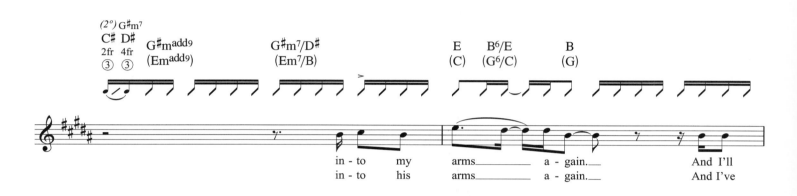

in - to my arms_____ a - gain.___ And I'll
in - to his arms_____ a - gain.___ And I've

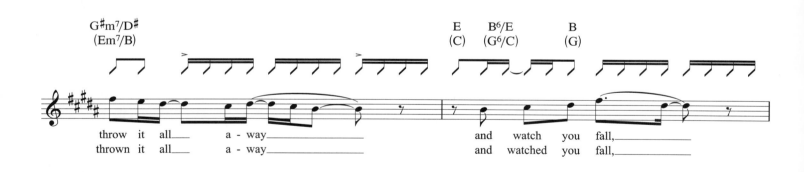

throw it all___ a - way_____ and watch you fall,_____
thrown it all___ a - way_____ and watched you fall,_____

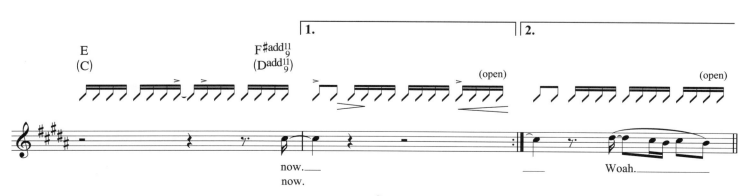

now.___
now.

Woah._____

49

Lego House

Words & Music by Ed Sheeran, Christopher Leonard & Jake Gosling

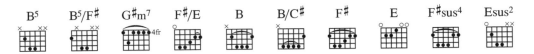

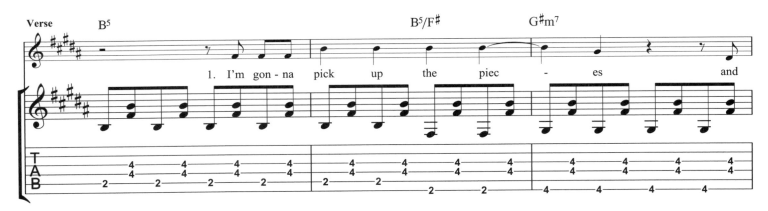

My three words have two mean-

-ings but there's one thing on my mind.

Fig. 1

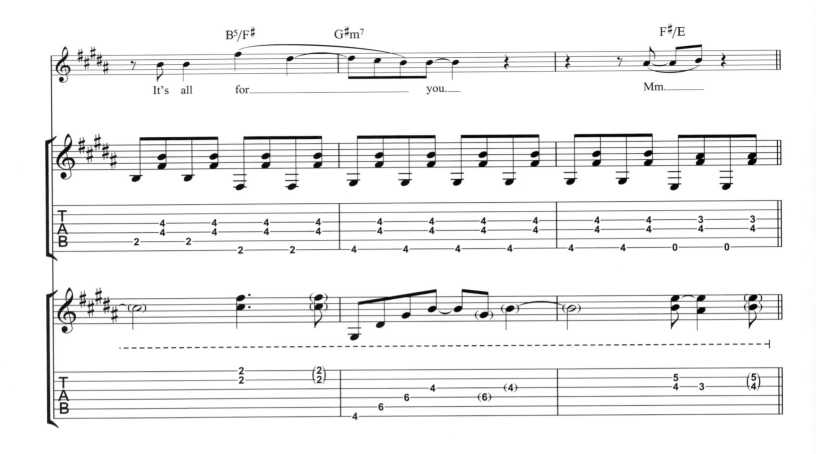

It's all for_____ you._____ Mm._____

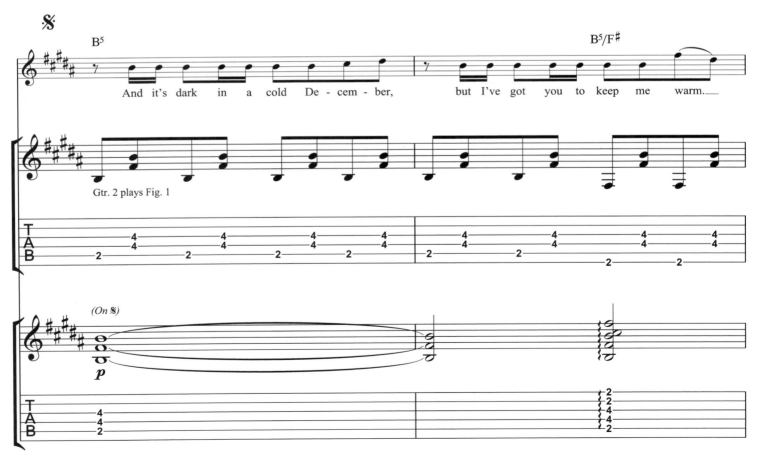

And it's dark in a cold De - cem - ber, but I've got you to keep me warm._____

Gtr. 2 plays Fig. 1

(On %)

If you're bro - ken I will mend you and I'll keep you shel-tered from the

storm that's rag - ing on now.

I'm out of touch, I'm out of love, I'll pick you up when you're get-ting down.

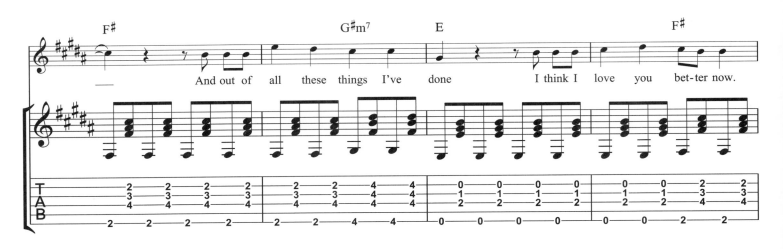

And out of all these things I've done I think I love you bet-ter now.

I'm out of sight, I'm out of mind, I'll do it all for you in time.

To Coda ⊕

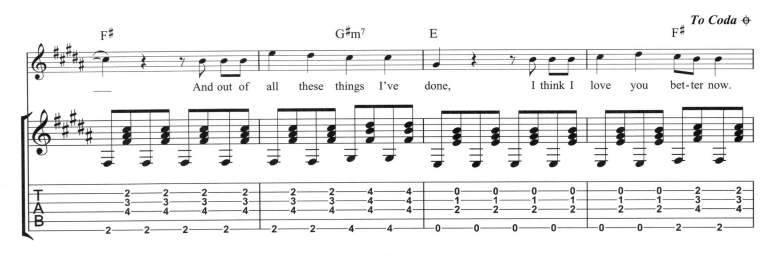

And out of all these things I've done, I think I love you bet-ter now.

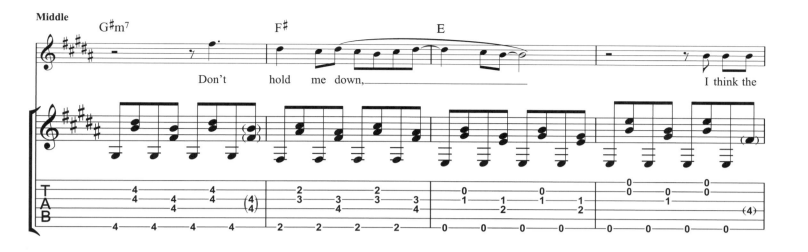

Middle

Don't hold me down,_____ I think the

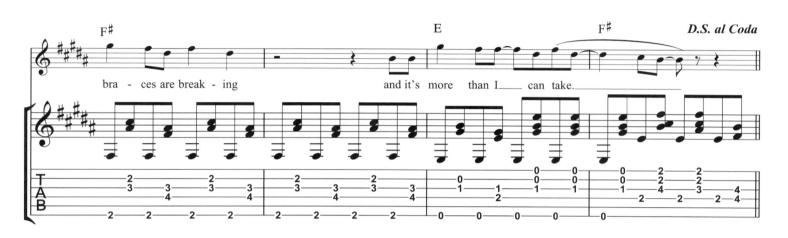

bra - ces are break - ing and it's more than I___ can take._____

D.S. al Coda

Coda

I'm out of touch, I'm out of love, I'll pick you up when you're get-ting down.___

p Gtr. 2 tacet

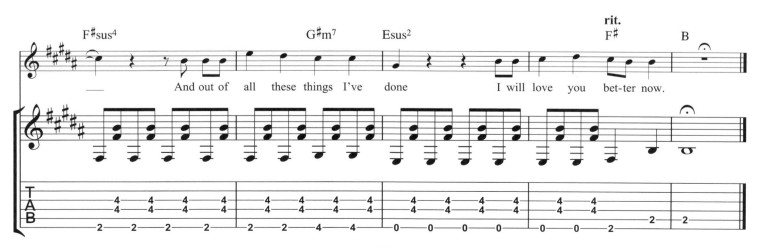

rit.

___ And out of all these things I've done I will love you bet-ter now.

57

Kiss Me

Words & Music by Ed Sheeran, Julie Frost & Justin Franks

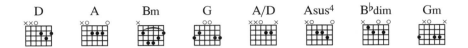

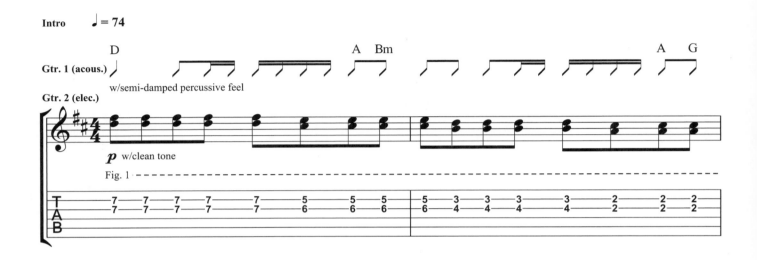

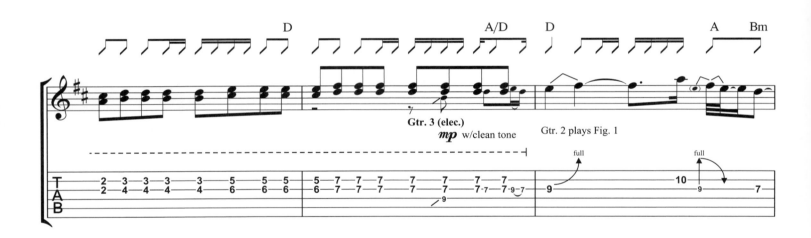

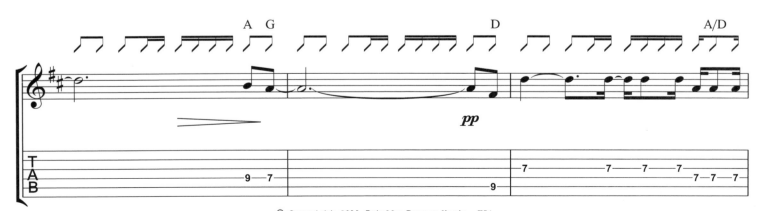

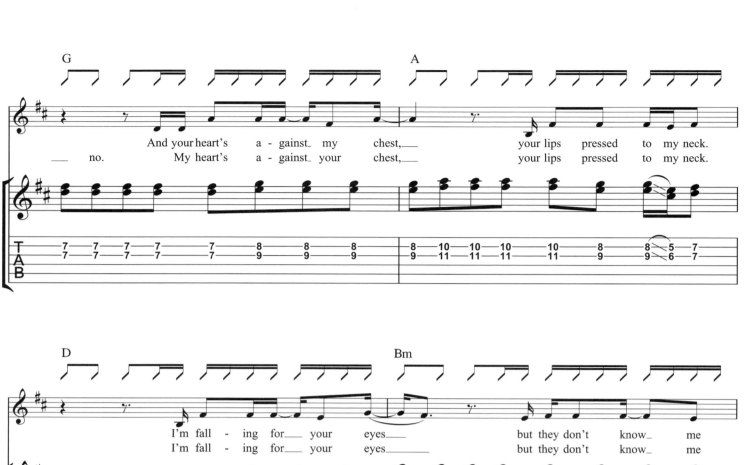

And your heart's a - gainst my chest,___ your lips pressed to my neck.
___ no. My heart's a - gainst your chest,___ your lips pressed to my neck.

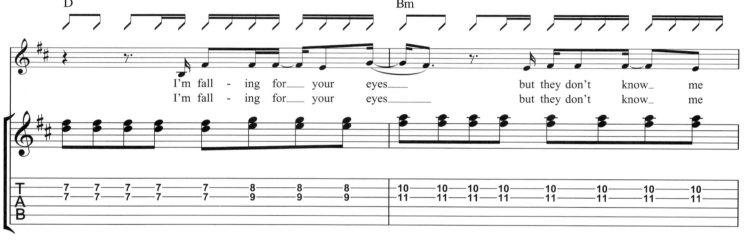

I'm fall - ing for___ your eyes___ but they don't know___ me
I'm fall - ing for___ your eyes_____ but they don't know___ me

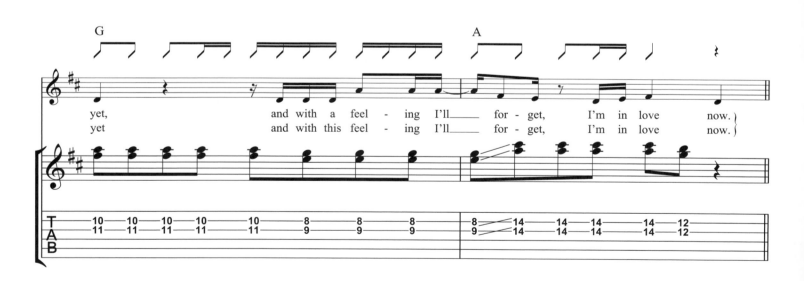

yet, and with a feel - ing I'll___ for - get, I'm in love now.}
yet and with this feel - ing I'll___ for - get, I'm in love now.}

Chorus

*Gtrs. 1+2

*composite part

Kiss me___ like you wan-na be loved, you wan-na be loved, you wan-na be

60

loved.   This___ feels___ like   fall-ing in love,___   fall-ing in

love,   fall - ing in love.___   Mm.___

let ring...

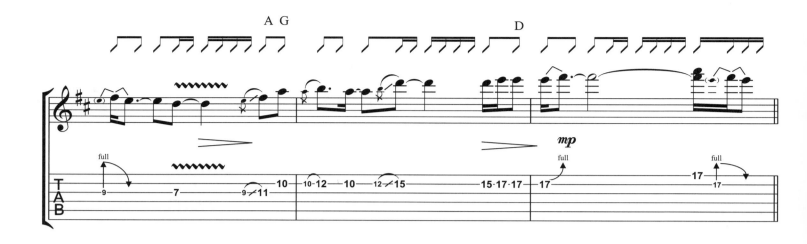

Bridge

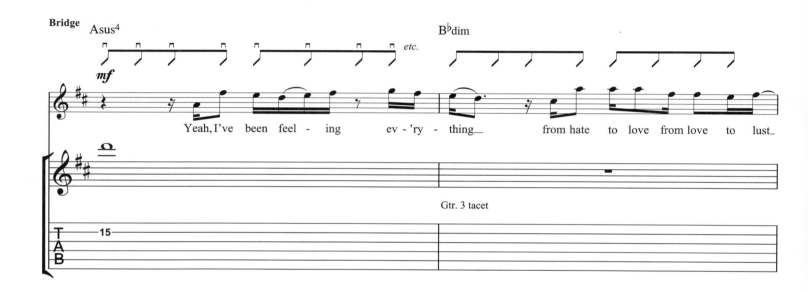

Yeah, I've been feel - ing ev - 'ry - thing___ from hate to love from love to lust___

Gtr. 3 tacet

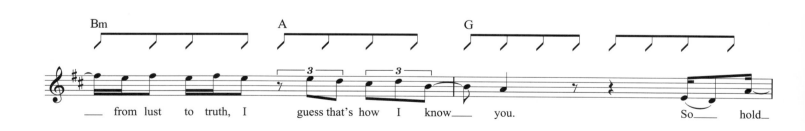

___ from lust to truth, I guess that's how I know___ you. So___ hold___

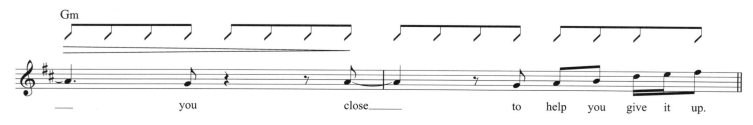

___ you close___ to help you give it up.

You Need Me, I Don't Need You

Words & Music by Ed Sheeran

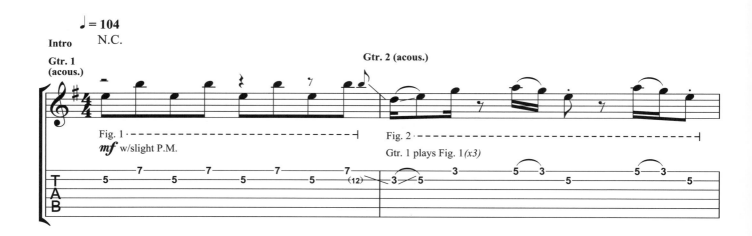

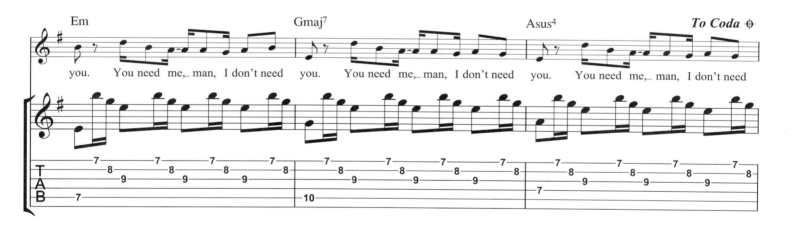

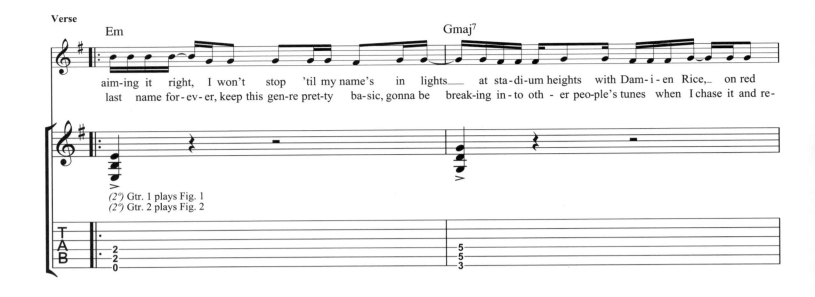

Verse

Em ... Gmaj7

aim-ing it right, I won't stop 'til my name's in lights ___ at sta-di-um heights with Dam-i-en Rice, ___ on red
last name for-ev-er, keep this gen-re pret-ty ba-sic, gonna be break-ing in-to oth-er peo-ple's tunes when I chase it and re-

(2°) Gtr. 1 plays Fig. 1
(2°) Gtr. 2 plays Fig. 2

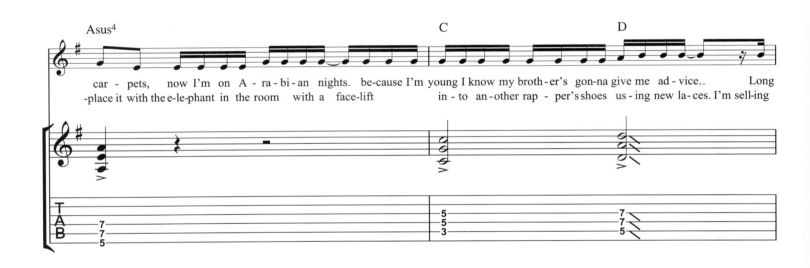

Asus4 ... C ... D

car - pets, now I'm on A - ra - bi - an nights ___ be-cause I'm young I know my broth-er's gon-na give me ad - vice. ___ Long
-place it with the e-le-phant in the room with a face-lift in - to an-oth-er rap - per's shoes us-ing new la - ces. I'm sell-ing

Em ... Gmaj7

night - er, short height and I've gone hy - per, nev - er be an - y-thing but a sin-ger-song - writ - er.
C. D.'s from my ruck-sack, aim-ing for the pa-pers, sell-ing C. D.'s from my ruck - sack aim-ing for the ma-jors. Na-tion-

68

Asus⁴ ... C ... D

Yeah, the game's ov - er but now I'm on a new lev - el, watch how I step on the track_ with-out a loop ped - al.
-wide tour with Just Jack_ still had to get the bus back, clean-cut_ kid_ with-out a ra - zor for the mous - tache. I

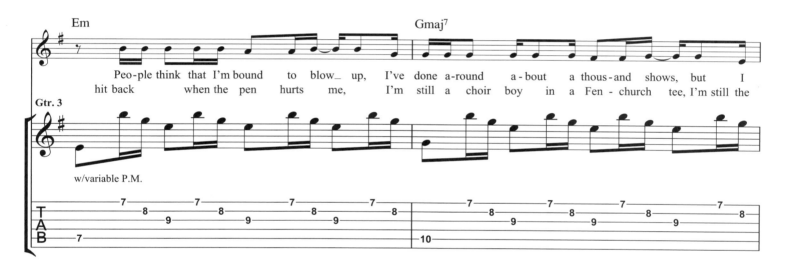

Em ... Gmaj⁷

Peo-ple think that I'm bound to blow_ up, I've done a-round a-bout a thous-and shows, but I
hit back when the pen hurts me, I'm still a choir boy in a Fen - church tee, I'm still the

Gtr. 3

w/variable P.M.

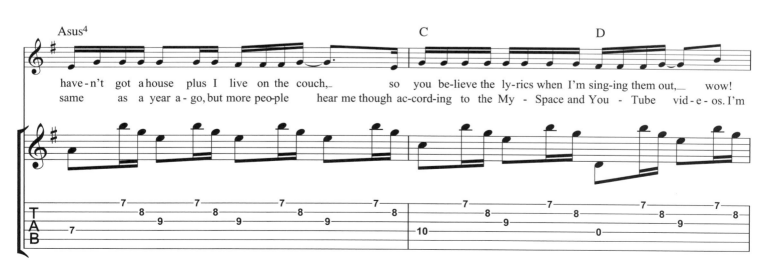

Asus⁴ ... C ... D

have-n't got a house plus I live on the couch,_ so you be-lieve the ly-rics when I'm sing-ing them out,_ wow!
same as a year a - go, but more peo-ple hear me though ac-cord-ing to the My - Space and You - Tube vid - e - os. I'm

69

From day one I've been pre-pared, with V O five wax for my gin - ger hair__ so now I'm
al-ways do-ing shows if I'm not I'm in the stu-di-o, tru-ly broke, never grow-ing up,__ call me Ruf-i-o,

back to the so-fa giving a dose of what the fut - ure holds.__'Cause it's an-oth-er day, plus I keep my
me-lo-dy mu-sic mak-er, read-ing all the pa-pers, they say I'm up- and-com-ing like I'm fuck-ing in an el-e-vat-or.

you at all. You need me,__ man, I don't_____ need you.

Give Me Love

Words & Music by Ed Sheeran, Christopher Leonard & Jake Gosling

*Symbols in parentheses represent chord names with respect to capoed gtr. (Tab 0 = 1st fret)
Symbols above represent actual sounding chords

73

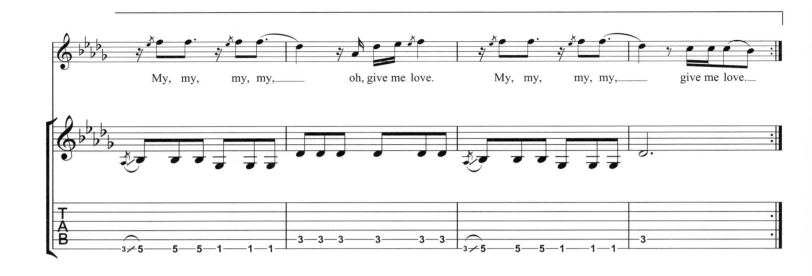

My, my, my, my, _____ oh, give me love. My, my, my, my, _____ give me love. _____

2.

Dᵇ (C)   Eᵇm (Dm)   Gᵇsus² (Fsus²)

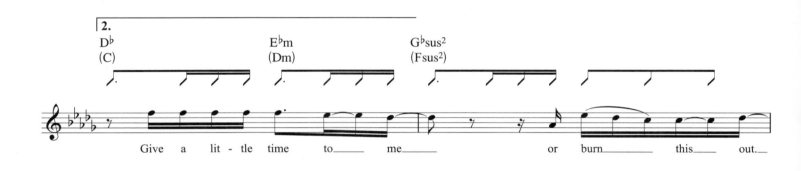

Give a lit - tle time to _____ me _____ or burn _____ this _____ out. _____

Dᵇ (C)   Eᵇm (Dm)   Gᵇsus² (Fsus²)   Dᵇ (C)   Eᵇm (Dm)

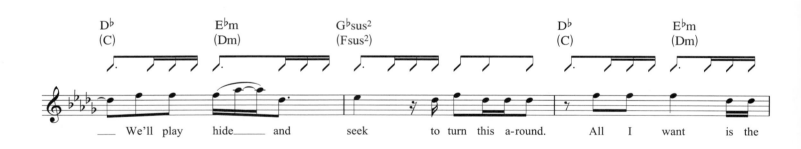

_____ We'll play hide _____ and seek to turn this a-round. All I want is the

Gᵇsus² (Fsus²)   Bᵇm (Am)   Aᵇ (G)   Gᵇ (F)

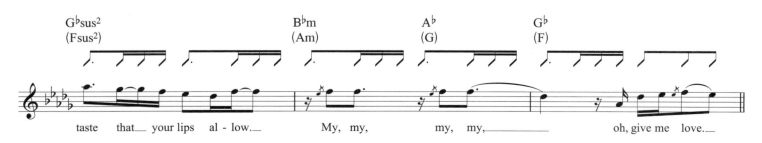

taste that _____ your lips al - low. _____ My, my, my, my, _____ oh, give me love. _____

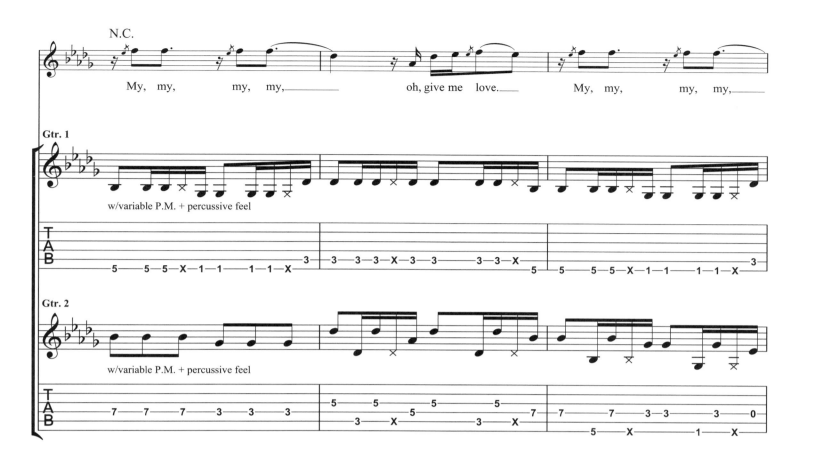

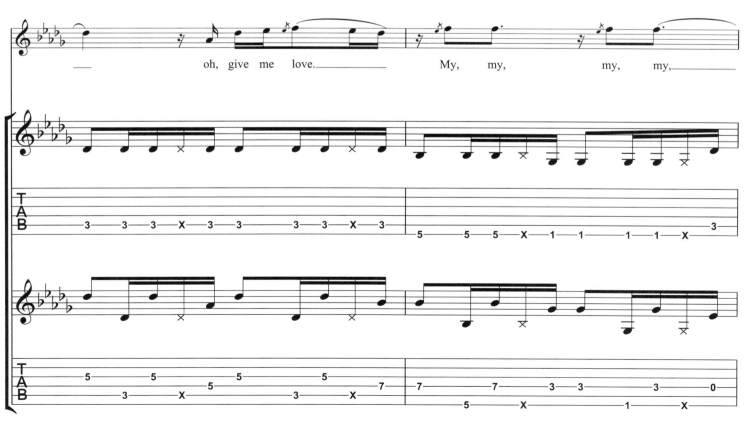

oh, give me love.   My, my,   my, my,_____   give me love.___

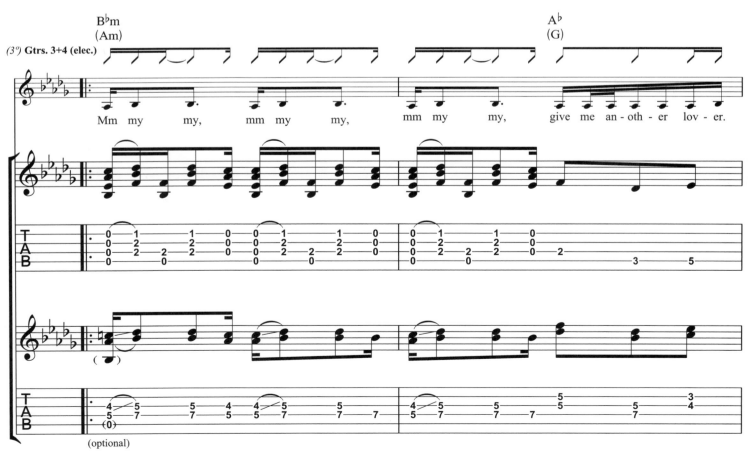

Mm my   my,   mm my   my,   mm my   my,   give me an-oth-er lov-er.

(3º) Gtrs. 3+4 (elec.)

B♭m
(Am)

A♭
(G)

(optional)

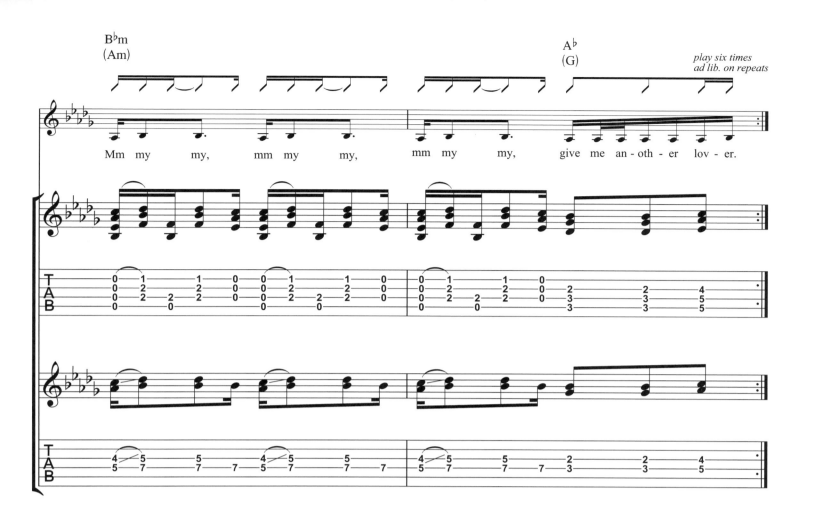

Mm my my, mm my my, mm my my, give me an-oth-er lov-er.

My my, my my,_____ oh, give me love._____ My my, my my,_____

Gtrs. 1-3 tacet

1-5.

— oh, give me love._____

6.

N.C.

— oh, give me love._____

The Parting Glass

Words & Music by Ed Sheeran, Jake Gosling & Peter Gosling

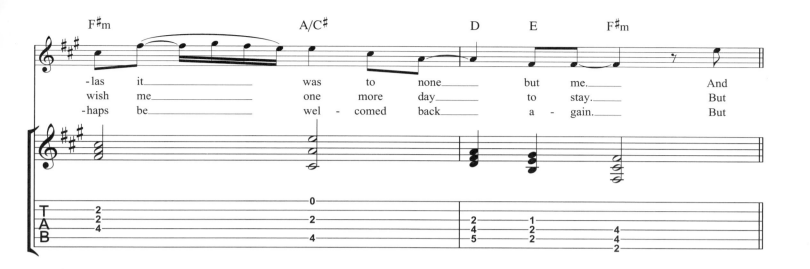

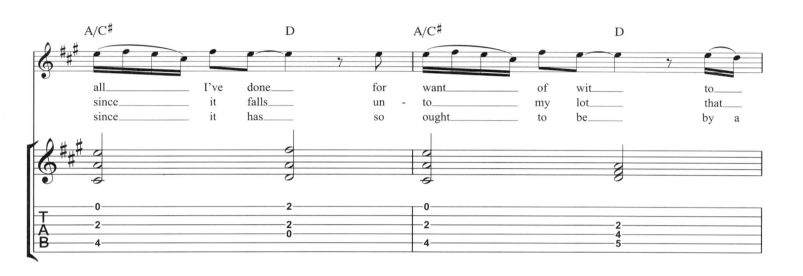

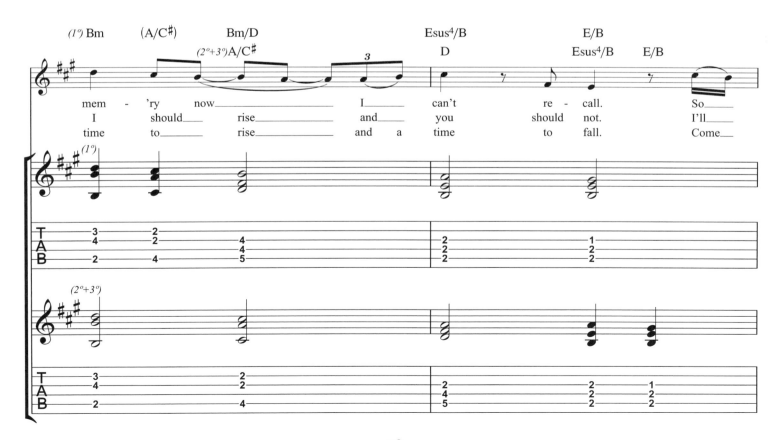

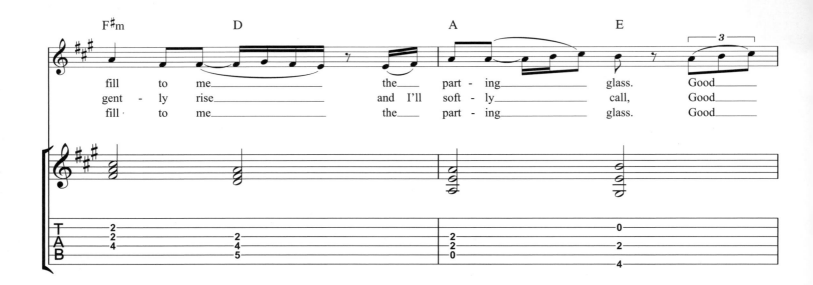

fill   to   me_____   the___ part - ing_____   glass.   Good_____
gent - ly rise_____   and I'll soft - ly_____   call,   Good_____
fill   to   me_____   the___ part - ing_____   glass.   Good_____

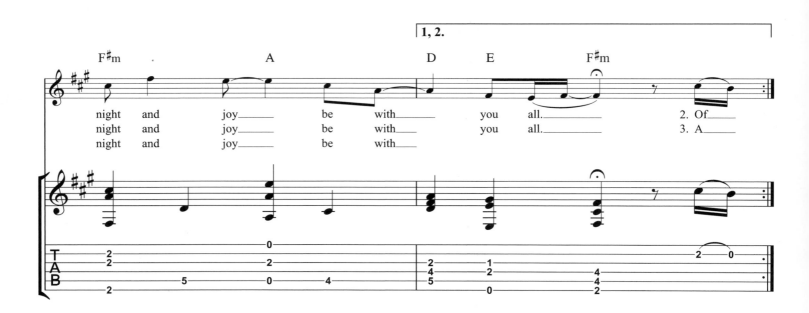

1, 2.

night and   joy_____   be   with_____   you all._____   2. Of_____
night and   joy_____   be   with_____   you all._____   3. A_____
night and   joy_____   be   with____

3.

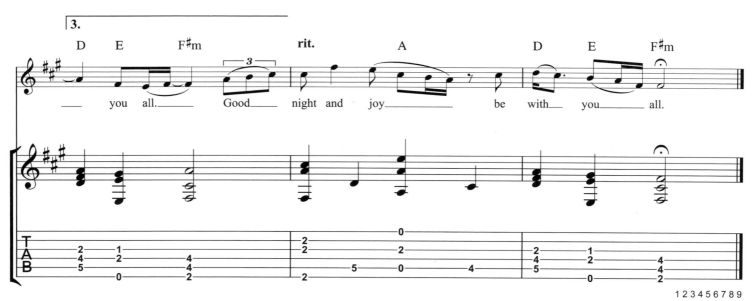

___ you all.____ Good____ night and joy_____   be with___ you____ all.

1 2 3 4 5 6 7 8 9